Contents

Gill & Macmillan
Hume Avenue
Park West
Dublin 12
www.gillmacmillan.ie

ISBN: 9780717153053
© Janna Tiearney 2012

Design: Outburst Design
Cover illustration: Aisli Madden
Inside illustrations: Derry Dillon

First published April 2012

Acknowledgments

'My Foot Fell Asleep' ©2009 Kenn Nesbitt from *My Hippo Has the Hiccups* by Kenn Nesbitt. Permission to reproduce this poem was granted by poetry4kids.com.

This edition of 'Washed Away', 'Overnight Train' and 'Big Ted's Barbecue' is published by arrangement with Macmillan Education Australia. Level 1, 15-19 Claremont, South Yarra, Victoria, Australia 3141.

'Over the Rainbow' Lyrics by E.Y. Harburg.

The Twits by Roald Dahl, published by Puffin Books. Permission to reproduce this excerpt was granted by David Higham Associates Ltd.

'When I'm Older' by Lemn Sissay from *Read Me and Laugh*, published by Macmillan Children's Books, 2005.

The publishers have made every effort to contact copyright holders but any omission will be rectified at the next reprint.

Going Shopping

Read this extract from the story 'Who Needs a Tail?'

Miss Fluffy had a nice little shop for animals. She sold ribbons for hairy dogs, diamond collars for cats and even powder puffs for rabbits whose tails were too small.

One day a small, brown creature came into the shop. He was very short, and he had to stand on tip-toe to see over the top.

'Good morning, sir,' said Miss Fluffy, 'and what can I do for you?'

'I want to see some tails,' said the small brown animal shyly.

'Of course,' said Miss Fluffy. 'Perhaps you'd like to see what we have. What sort of tail were you thinking of buying? We have bushy tails, curly tails, long and short tails…'

Write a list of things that Miss Fluffy's shop might sell to animals.

Shopping List

_____

_____

_____

Answer the questions. Use full sentences.

Who owned the little shop for animals?

_____

Describe the animal that first came into the shop.

_____

What did he want to buy?

_____

Did he buy what he was looking for? Why/why not?

_____

_____

What kind of tail do you think would suit the guinea pig?

_____

What else do you think the guinea pig could have bought?

_____

Unscramble the sentences. Write the correct sentences and don't forget to use capital letters and full stops.

shop Miss had Fluffy little a

_____

tail the buy little wanted to animal a

_____

laughed guinea Henry the at pig Hare

_____

Draw the tails on these animals. Label the animals too.

horse, shark, cat, pig, bird, rabbit

Make up your own animal with a lovely tail. Draw the animal and give it a name.

Finish the sentences.

The fox has a very bushy _____.

I _____ like carrots but Mum said they are good for me.

You should _____ brush your teeth twice a day.

The guinea pig is a little _____.

I got all my spellings _____ today.

I _____ like to go to your party.

Choose by or buy.

Example: She went to the city **by** train.
            My friend is going to **buy** a puppy.

I will _____ a book with my money.

We went for a walk _____ the lake.

My cousin came from Dublin _____ bus.

The school is going to _____ new goals.

The song words were written _____ Bono.

She wants to _____ a new computer game.

We use a capital letter at the beginning of a sentence and a full stop at the end of the sentence.

Circle the letters that should be capital letters and add full stops to the sentences.

the supermarket is very big

my brother is walking to the shop

the children are drawing pictures

my friend and I are going to the cinema

we like going to school every day

Write three of your own sentences about shopping. Draw a picture to match one of your sentences.

_____

_____

_____

_____

You are having a sleepover at your house. Write a list of things that you might need to buy.

To buy

_____

_____

_____

_____

_____

_____

_____

_____

_____

_____

_____

2

My Foot Fell Asleep

Read the poem.

My foot fell asleep
right inside of my shoe
from sitting around
having nothing to do.
It hadn't drank warm milk
nor tried to count sheep;
it just wasn't busy,
and fell right asleep.

You see, in my shoe
it gets lonely and boring,
which made my foot sleepy,
and soon it was snoring.
My foot snored so loudly
my shoe began flapping.
But it didn't notice –
it kept right on napping!

Now I'm in my bed
and I've been up all night.
I'm trying to sleep,
although try as I might,
my foot slept all day
(what a foolish mistake!)
now I can't fall asleep
'cause my foot's wide awake!

(Kenn Nesbitt)

Answer the questions.

Why did his foot fall asleep?

It had _____.

What did it not drink?

It did not _____.

Where does it get lonely and boring?

It gets lonely and boring _____.

Why did the shoe start flapping?

It started flapping because _____.

Why can't he fall asleep?

He can't fall asleep because _____.

What could you do if your foot fell asleep?

_____

Match the parts of the poem.

it just wasn't busy	and I've been up all night.
But it didn't notice	what a foolish mistake!
Now I'm in bed	it kept right on napping!
my foot slept all day	and fell right asleep.

8

Finish the sentences.

right, which, made, been, snoring, asleep, shoe

I have _____ doing my homework every night.

Jenny fell _____ on the sofa.

You must turn _____ at the traffic lights.

I do not know _____ book to read first.

Mum _____ my favourite dinner.

My sister said I was _____ loudly last night.

The dog ran away with my _____.

Write your own sentence using the word **right**.

_____

Write your own sentence using the word **shoe**.

_____

Circle the rhyming words in this verse.

My foot fell asleep

right inside of my shoe

from sitting around

having nothing to do.

It hadn't drank warm milk

nor tried to count sheep;

it just wasn't busy,

and fell right asleep.

Find words in the poem that rhyme with these words

all _____   right _____

sleep _____   you _____

say _____   boring _____

flapping _____   cry _____

how _____

Can you think of a word that rhymes with your name? _____

We use a capital letter at the beginning of a sentence and a full stop at the end of a sentence. The names of people and pets also start with a capital letter.

Underline the capital letters in the sentences then write a sentence of your own.

Lorraine and Helen are doing their homework.

We went to Harry's house to see his puppy.

The dog Rex is sleeping on the sofa.

Pat bought a game and Jim bought a football.

The teacher asked Sharon to ring the bell.

_____

Write over the letters that should be capital letters and add full stops to these sentences.

my brother's name is killian

we are planting trees at school

my cat jack likes to sleep by the fire

ben and gemma are having their lunch

he invited tom to his party

Write a sentence about your friend.

_____

Finish the poem using your own words. Try to rhyme the 2nd and 4th lines.

Do your rough work below.

My _____ fell asleep

_____

_____

_____

Now write your poem neatly.

_____

_____

_____

_____

Draw a picture to match your poem.

3

(**Washed Away**)

Read this extract from the story.

'You cannot play in the kitchen,' she said. 'It is not a safe place to play.'

Stan did not want to listen to his mum. 'I do not care what she says. I like to play in the kitchen,' he said. So Stan went to play there.

He played on the plates. He played on the cups. He played on the knives and forks, too.

'I want to play in the sink,' said Stan. So he went to play there.

'Yuck! A spider,' said a voice. Then someone turned on the tap. 'Oh, no!' said Stan. 'Water is falling. I do not like water.'

Can you find these words? Underline them.

> **cannot, kitchen, place, want, listen, says,
> went, forks, so, spider, someone, water**

Write a different title for the story.

_____

Answer the questions.

Where did Stan like to play?

_____

Where did Stan play first?

_____

Where was there water falling?

_____

Who came to help Stan?

_____

Where did Stan and his Mum go?

_____

Where does Stan play now?

_____

Do you think Stan will play in the kitchen again? _____

Where would be an unsafe place for you to play?

_____

Finish the sentences.

sink, fast, pulled, safe, on

Stan's Mum said the kitchen was not a _____ place.

Stan played in the _____.

Someone switched _____ the tap.

The water was going _____.

Mum _____ Stan out of the drain.

14

Write the odd one out.

blackbird, crow, cat, robin

_____

apple, carrot, banana, strawberry

_____

oak, chestnut, beech, sunflower

_____

lion, rhinoceros, hamster, monkey

_____

Cork, London, Wexford, Cavan

_____

money, five, eleven, three

_____

shirt, cheese, trousers, dress

_____

table, chair, book, bed

_____

Complete the wordsearch.

> pull, their, liked, kitchen, there, spider,
> faster, pulled, told, outside, water, sink

e	m	c	a	t	e	k	u	k	o
p	k	a	x	h	x	i	p	k	u
f	a	s	t	e	r	t	u	k	t
t	h	e	i	r	e	c	l	j	s
r	s	o	y	e	i	h	l	l	i
t	p	p	u	l	l	e	d	i	d
o	i	f	j	x	j	n	w	k	e
l	d	g	s	i	n	k	k	e	e
d	e	j	h	y	a	k	m	d	t
d	r	k	b	p	w	a	t	e	r

We use a capital letter for the word I.

Circle the letters that should be capital letters. Add full stops to the end of the sentences.

i wish i could get a kitten

i hope that rachel and i can play outside

conor and i are playing football after school

i like school but i can't wait for the holidays

patrick said i could borrow his game

We also use capital letters for the names of places.

Write these places.

The country you live in   _____

The county you live in   _____

The town/area you live in   _____

Your school   _____

A country   _____

A city   _____

A planet   _____

A shop   _____

Write to or too in the sentences.

'I told you not _____ play in the kitchen,' said Stan's mum.

The water washed Stan _____ the drain.

He played on the knives and forks, _____.

'I want _____ play in the sink,' said Stan.

Stan did not want _____ listen _____ his mum.

Write your own sentences with the words to, too and two.

_____

_____

_____

17

Label this spider.

web, leg, fangs, eyes, hairs

Stan did not listen to his Mum's rules. Write 5 rules for the classroom.

_____

_____

_____

_____

_____

_____

_____

4

Popcorn

Draw a picture for each of these sentences.

Popcorn is one of our favourite snacks.

Popcorn comes from a maize plant.

Popcorn is good for you if you do not add much salt, butter or sugar.

Popcorn can pop one metre into the air.

Do you like popcorn? Write two sentences about why you like it or don't like it.

_____

_____

Think of an interesting popcorn flavour.

_____

Answer the questions. Use full sentences.

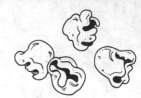

Where is most of the world's popcorn grown?

_____

How long does it take for the popcorn seed to start growing?

_____

How many shapes of popcorn are there?

_____

When was the largest popcorn ball made?

_____

Do you like sweet or salty popcorn?

_____

Describe popcorn using your own words.

Popcorn is _____.

Finish the sentences.

bigger, water, while, salt, popcorn, kilograms

The plant needs _____ and sunlight to grow.

Popcorn is good for you if you don't add too much sugar, _____ or butter.

Snowflake popcorn is used at the cinema because it pops _____.

In the 1980s microwave _____ was invented.

The largest popcorn ball weighed nearly 2,300 _____.

It is nice to eat popcorn _____ you watch a movie.

Find smaller words in these words.

because _____

best _____

popcorn _____

sit _____

plant _____

sunlight _____

vitamins _____

mushroom _____

Write your own sentences using these words.

because

_____

_____

best

_____

_____

Write your own question using the word **why**. Don't forget the question mark.

_____

_____

Days of the week, months of the year and special days start with a capital letter.

Underline the mistakes in the sentences.

It is st. patrick's day on 17th march.

Jenny's birthday is in august.

The school is closing on wednesday

I wake up very early on christmas day.

I can't wait for halloween in october.

Write two sentences of your own with days or months.

_____

_____

Answer the questions.

What day of the week is it today?   _____

What day is tomorrow?   _____

What day was it yesterday?   _____

What is your favourite day of the week?   _____

What month is it now?   _____

When is your birthday?   _____

These instructions to make popcorn are all mixed up. Write the correct sentence by the pictures.

Be careful! It is hot. Open the bag as shown on the packet.

Listen! When popping is 1 to 2 seconds between pops, the popcorn is done.

Microwave on high power for 2 to 4 minutes.

Place the bag in the microwave, front face down.

Take the bag out of the microwave.

Write your own book about popcorn.

Write one sentence and draw a picture on each page.

Do your rough work below.

Popcorn

By: _____

_____

_____

_____

_____

_____

_____

_____

_____

_____

5

Sing the song.

Somewhere over the rainbow
Way up high,
There's a land that I heard of
Once in a lullaby.

Somewhere over the rainbow
Skies are blue,
And the dreams that you dare to dream
Really do come true.

Someday I'll wish upon a star
And wake up where the clouds are far
Behind me.
Where troubles melt like lemon drops
Away above the chimney tops
That's where you'll find me.

Somewhere over the rainbow
Bluebirds fly.
Birds fly over the rainbow.
Why then, oh why can't I?

If happy little bluebirds fly
Beyond the rainbow
Why, oh why can't I?

Underline the words that rhyme in the same colour.

How many times does the word 'rainbow' appear in this text? _____

Complete the part of the song.

Someday I'll wish upon a _____

And wake up _____ the clouds are far

Behind me.

Where troubles melt _____ lemon drops

Away _____ the chimney tops

That's where you'll _____ me.

Somewhere _____ the rainbow

Bluebirds fly.

Birds fly over the _____.

Why then, oh _____ can't I?

If _____ little bluebirds fly

Beyond the rainbow

Why, oh why _____ I?

Which is your favourite line from the song?

_____

_____

Unscramble the words to make sentences from the song. Write the sentences. Use capital letters and full stops.

wish upon some I'll a star day

_____

over birds rainbow fly the

_____

Now write one of your own sentences about rainbows.

_____

Complete the crossword.

rainbow, over, high, land, dream, star, somewhere, wish, upon, why

Down

1. Fairytales often start with 'Once _____ a time'

2. You do this while you are sleeping.

3. Something that shines at night in the sky.

5. You make this when you see a shooting star.

6. Opposite of under

9. Opposite of low

Across

4. An arch of colours that forms in the sky

7. Fish live in water, birds live on _____

8. some+where

10. A question word

27

We use a question mark (?) when we write a question.

Write a full stop or a question mark for each of these sentences.

I had cereal and yoghurt for breakfast

Where did you put my reading book

When did you get a new skateboard

Sean is learning his spellings

Why were you late for school

Who is going to the party

Write the correct question word. Add question marks.

which, where, why, who, what

_____ is playing the piano

_____ is Peter laughing

_____ pen belongs to you

_____ time is break

_____ is the match this weekend

Write a question for this answer.

It is on Friday.

Question: _____

Colour the rainbow using the correct colours.

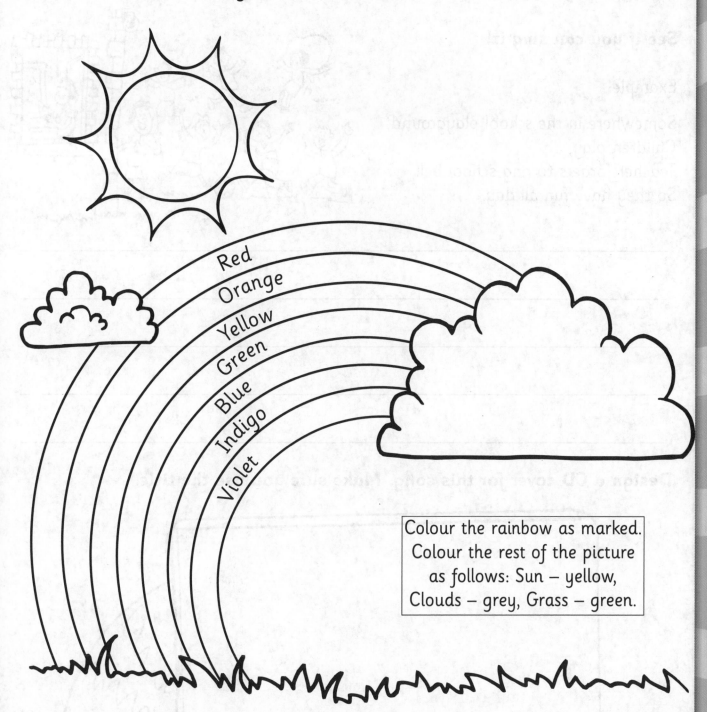

Red
Orange
Yellow
Green
Blue
Indigo
Violet

Colour the rainbow as marked.
Colour the rest of the picture
as follows: Sun – yellow,
Clouds – grey, Grass – green.

Draw and label something that is each of these colours:

red   yellow

orange   violet

Change the first verse of the song. Start the song with 'Somewhere.....'

See if you can sing it!

Example:

Somewhere in the school playground,
Children play,
Teacher forgets to ring school bell,
So they have fun all day.

_____

_____

_____

_____

_____

Design a CD cover for this song. Make sure you use the title.

6

Overnight Train

Read this extract from the story.

I was on the train to Granny's house. When I looked out of the window, I saw a car. The car had a girl in it.

I waved at the girl. The girl waved at me.

When I looked out of the window, I saw a bird. The bird flew close to the train. It flew up into the sky.

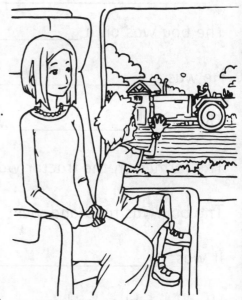

When I looked out of the window, I saw a scarecrow in a field. The scarecrow had a shirt on. The scarecrow had a straw hat and a scarf, too.

When I looked out of the window, I saw a farmer. The farmer was on a tractor. The tractor was orange. The farmer was smiling.

When I looked out of the window, it was dark. It was night. Lights were on in houses. I was tired. I went to sleep.

Write numbers in the boxes to show the order of things that the boy saw. You may have to read the whole story to check.

☐ park

☐ bird

☐ man with a dog

☐ scarecrow

☐ car

☐ Granny

☐ farmer

Finish the sentences.

looking, morning, train, their, sleep, scarecrow, smiling

The boy was on a _____.

He was _____ out of the window.

The _____ was in the field.

The farmer on the tractor was _____.

The boy was tired and went to _____.

It was _____ when he woke up.

He saw children and _____ mums and dads.

Answer the questions. Use full sentences.

What did he do when he saw the girl in the car?

_____

Name one thing the scarecrow was wearing.

_____

What colour was the tractor?

_____

What did the boy see in the water?

_____

Who was waiting for the train?

_____

Do you think the boy enjoyed the train journey? Say why.

_____

Where would you like to go on a train?

_____

Change some of the types of transport in this poem to make your own poem. Try to make some of the words rhyme as below.

Take a <u>bike</u> or take a <u>train</u>,

Take a <u>ship</u> or take a <u>plane</u>,

Take a <u>camel</u>, take a <u>hike</u>,

Take a <u>jet</u> or take a <u>bike</u>.

Take a <u>rocket</u> to the <u>moon</u>,

But please be sure to come home soon!

submarine

elephant

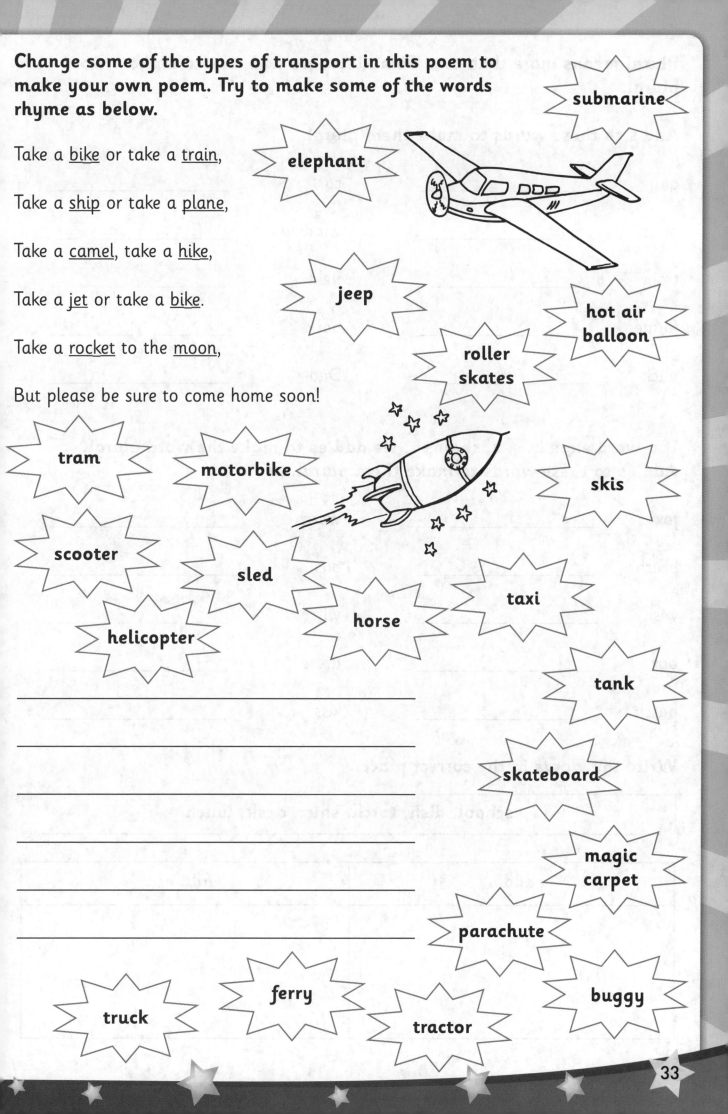

jeep

hot air balloon

roller skates

tram

motorbike

skis

scooter

sled

taxi

horse

helicopter

tank

skateboard

magic carpet

parachute

ferry

buggy

truck

tractor

_____

_____

_____

_____

_____

Plural means more than one. Sometimes we add an s to make a word plural.

Add s to these words to make them plural.

girl _____   car _____

house _____   window _____

train _____   field _____

farmer _____   park _____

duck _____   Dad _____

If a word ends in s, x, sh or ch, we add es to make the word plural. Add es to these words to make them plural.

fox _____   watch _____

brush _____   bus _____

wish _____   witch _____

box _____   dress _____

patch _____   kiss _____

Write the words in the correct place.

school, dish, torch, shirt, desk, lunch

add s	add es

Write sentences to show what each of these people own.

Remember to use apostrophes.

The first one has been done for you.

Granny   Mum   the farmer

This is Granny's house.

_____

_____

Write a sentence to show what your friend owns.

_____

_____

Draw the picture.

Write directions to get from the school to the train station.

_____

_____

_____

_____

_____

7

Peter and the Wolf

Read this part of the story.

One day, Peter went for a walk and he met his friend, Duck, along the way.

Robin came to say hello to both Peter and Duck. When Robin flew down, Cat was about to pounce on the bird.

'Watch out!' cried Peter.

Robin flew up the tree and Cat missed.

Peter went back home.

'Stay at home, Peter. There is a hungry wolf around,' said Grandad.

The hungry wolf was prowling outside. He found Duck and pounced upon the duck and ate him.

Peter looked out of his window and he saw the wolf trying to catch Robin and Cat. They were up on a tree.

Peter ran to help Robin and Cat. He quickly made a plan to use a rope to help. He climbed up the tree to Robin and Cat.

Can you find these words? Underline them.

> friend, both, when, about, cried, back,
> around, found, upon, trying, were, made, use, help

Name all the characters in the story. Circle the main character.

_____

_____

Write true or false.

Peter and Robin were friends. _____

Cat ate Robin. _____

Grandad told Peter to stay at home. _____

Peter ran to help Robin and Duck. _____

Peter used a rope to catch the wolf. _____

The wolf ate Peter and Grandad. _____

Answer the questions. Use full sentences.

Why did Peter's Grandad want him to stay at home?

_____

What did Peter use to help Robin and Cat?

_____

Who flew at the wolf?

_____

What happened to the wolf?

_____

Can you think of another story that has a bad wolf in it?

_____

What would you have done when you saw the wolf?

_____

Name some things we have to be careful of when we play outside.

_____

Finish the sentences.

> **made, both, around, its, upon, gave, use**

The children ran _____ the field.

My friend _____ me a book for my birthday.

Once _____ a time, there was a princess called Daisy.

_____ the mobile phone to call home.

Mum and I _____ chicken for dinner.

The cat was chasing _____ tail.

My sister and I were _____ looking forward to Easter.

Find smaller words in these words.

branch _____

grandad _____

looking _____

upon _____

Write their or there.

Example: **There** are five teachers in my school. They each have **their** own laptop.

I went to see _____ new games.

I think your homework is over _____.

_____ are 25 children in the class.

_____ coats are covered in paint.

Nouns are naming words. Nouns can be names, places or things.

Examples of nouns: duck, bird, wolf, tree, Peter, Ireland

Underline the nouns in the sentences.

The duck was swimming in the pond.

Peter was afraid of the wolf.

Our classroom has blue chairs.

Wicklow is a county in Ireland.

My cat likes to curl up in the basket by the fire.

Read the nouns. Write the odd one out.

water, milk, orange juice, bread, tea _____

nest, sty, hedgehog, stable, den _____

Germany, China, Ireland, France, Spain _____

cheetah, rhino, elephant, parrot, zebra _____

purple, green, rainbow, orange, white _____

Fill in your own nouns.

At the shop I bought a blue _____.

The teacher will bring a _____ to the school.

I left my _____ on the _____.

I am going to _____ tonight.

What are they saying?

Pretend you are the wolf in the story of Peter and the Wolf.

Write about what happened.

_____

_____

_____

_____

_____

_____

_____

_____

_____

_____

8

Read the extract from the story *The Twits* by Roald Dahl.

Mr Twit didn't even bother to open his mouth wide when he ate. As a result (and because he never washed) there were always hundreds of bits of old breakfasts and lunches and suppers sticking to the hairs of his face. They weren't big bits, mind you, because he used to wipe those off with the back of his hand or on his sleeve while he was eating. But if you looked closely (not that you'd ever want to) you would see tiny specks of dried-up scrambled eggs stuck to the hairs, and spinach and tomato ketchup and fish fingers and minced chicken livers and all the other disgusting things Mr Twit liked to eat.

Think about all the things you have eaten in the last week. If you had a beard and you never washed, what things might be stuck in your beard?

_____

_____

_____

_____

_____

_____

Draw it too.

Answer the questions. Use full sentences.

How old was Mr Twit?

_____

What did Mr Twit think of himself?

_____

Name three things that could be found in Mr Twit's beard.

_____

Was Mr Twit a clean man? How do you know?

_____

Why is harder to clean your face when you have a beard?

_____

What do you think of Mr Twit?

_____

What advice would you give him?

_____

This piece of writing is full of mistakes. There are missing capital letters, full stops and question marks. There are also some incorrect capital letters. Can you mark it? Correct the mistakes.

I read the story about mr twit i Enjoyed the story but I think that he is very dirty

my friend jamie said Mr twit looked like his uncle ben. I wonder if mr Twit lives in

ireland as I would not like to meet him. I just wish that he would have a good

wash I wash myself Every day what about you

Use the words in the word box to complete the sentences.

tufts, one, was, thick, face

Mr Twit was _____ of these very hairy-faced men. The whole of his

_____ except for his forehead, his eyes and his nose _____

covered with _____ hair. The stuff even sprouted in revolting

_____ out of his nostrils and ear-holes.

Look these words up in a dictionary. Write the definition and your own sentence with each of them.

revolting _____

_____

twit _____

_____

matted_____

_____

cling_____

_____

specks _____

_____

Read this cartoon.

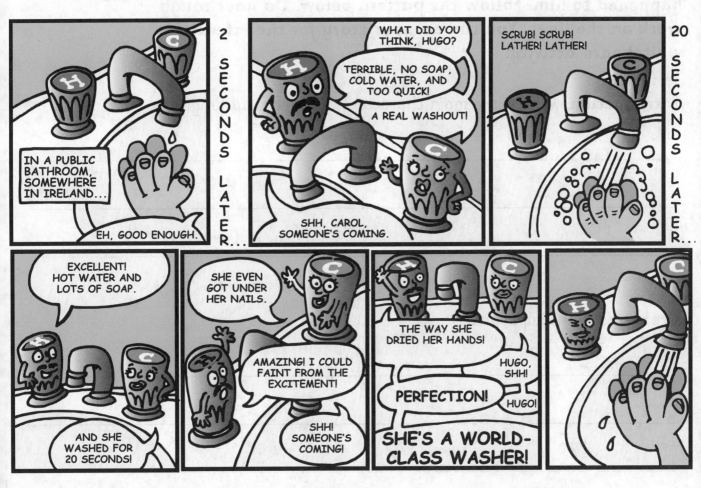

Write a list of things you should do when you wash your hands.

_____

_____

_____

_____

_____

_____

_____

_____

_____

_____

Write your own story about **Mr Twit** and something that happened to him. Follow the pattern below. Do your rough work on the lines. You can do your story for the interactive whiteboard activity.

Introduction: Who is the main character? ... Where did he go? ...

_____

_____

_____

Problem: What happened? ...

_____

_____

_____

Complication: What happened next? ... What did he decide to do?

_____

_____

_____

_____

Resolution: How did it end? How did he feel? ...

_____

_____

_____

9

Homes Around the World

Read this extract.

People live in different homes. People live in houses, apartments, caravans, yurts and tents.

There are many castles in Ireland. Long ago, only kings and queens lived in castles.

Houseboats are also homes. They are boats often made out of wood, and they stay on the water.

Yurts are made from wood and felt and are used by nomads in Mongolia. It is easy to move the yurt from place to place.

Look at this house plan.

How many bedrooms are there in this house?_____

What room is on the left of the kitchen? _____

How many bathrooms are there? _____

Is there a place to park a car? _____

How many doors are there in this house? _____

What room would you like to add to this house? _____

Answer the questions. Use full sentences.

Are there any castles in Ireland?

_____

What are houseboats often made out of?

_____

What is easy when you live in a yurt?

_____

Why do some people build their houses on stilts?

_____

Why do many houses in Ireland have sloped roofs?

_____

What kind of house would you like to live in?

_____

Describe what your home looks like.

_____

Finish the sentences.

Africa, houses, Australia, rain

In _____, some people live in huts.

In Spain, the roofs are flat because it does not _____ very much.

In Finland, many _____ are built out of wood.

Many people live in single storey houses in _____.

Choose the correct word. Write the sentence.

There are (much, many, lots) children playing games.

_____

Milkshakes are (made, make, mixed) from milk and ice-cream.

_____

I took (there, they, their) dog for a walk.

_____

She jumped (of, off, for) the diving board into the pool.

_____

He (does, goes, breaks) his homework every night.

_____

I (witch, which, wish) that it was the summer holidays.

_____

Write a short advert for a house for sale. It can be any kind of house!

_____

_____

_____

_____

_____

_____

Verbs are doing or action words.
Examples of verbs: live, run, play, watch, sing, write, is, jump, draw

Underline the verbs in the sentences.

Sally jumps on the trampoline.

The teacher talks to the children.

The dog barks all night.

I eat a sandwich for lunch.

We read stories every Friday.

Choose the correct verb. Write the sentence.

I (wish, watch, look) television after my homework is done.

_____

The teacher (laughs, sleeps, shouts) when we are bold.

_____

In the morning, I like to (drink, eat, wash) orange juice.

_____

Mum (bakes, swims, walks) chocolate cake.

_____

What things do you do at school? Write some verbs.

_____

_____

_____

What do you do in the different rooms? Write 5 sentences.

Example:
In the living room, I watch TV.

In the kitchen _____

_____

_____

_____

Draw and label a house that you would like to live in. Describe it.

yurt

caravan

houseboat

hut

house

treehouse

There are sayings about homes.

HOME SWEET HOME

Home is where the heart is

Make up your own saying about home.

10

When I'm Older

Read this part of the poem.

I'll never clean my bedroom. Never change my socks

I'll always yell 'OI!' through the letter box

I'll never wash the pots. I'll never do my bed.

For breakfast I'll only eat jam on shortbread

I'll never wipe my feet, I'll never wipe my nose

I'll never cut my nails and I'll never wash my clothes

I'll always ring the doorbell, I'll never wear a tie

I'll always answer the telephone with the word

Goodbye!

(Lemn Sissay)

Can you find these words? Underline them.

never, always, wash, breakfast, only, feet, ring, word

Underline the words that rhyme in the same colour.

Answer the questions. Use full sentences.

goodbye

What will he have first at the dinner table?

_____

What will he rush?

_____

What will he never brush?

_____

When Mum asks where he is going, what will he say?

_____

What will he eat for breakfast?

_____

What will he say when he answers the telephone?

_____

What was your favourite part of the poem?

_____

Do you think this child will really not do these things when he gets older? Explain.

_____

_____

What would you like to ask the person who wrote the poem?

_____

_____

Choose words from the box. Write the sentences.

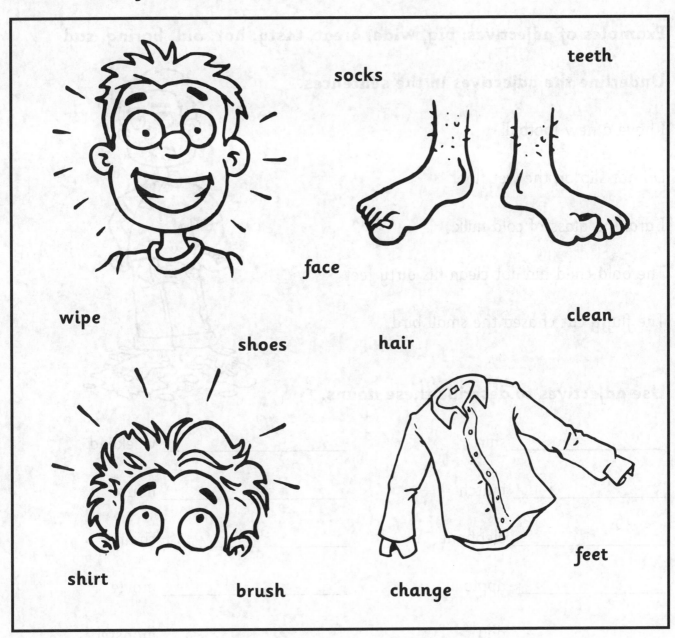

socks

teeth

face

wipe

clean

shoes

hair

shirt

brush

change

feet

I will clean my feet.

_____

_____

_____

_____

_____

Adjectives are describing words. They describe nouns.

Examples of adjectives: big, wide, great, tasty, hot, old, boring, sad

Underline the adjectives in the sentences.

I have a new football.

Do not slip on the wet floor.

I drank a glass of cold milk.

The bold child did not clean his dirty feet.

The fluffy cat chased the small bird.

Use adjectives to describe these nouns.

_____ shirt   _____ weekend

_____ match   _____ house

_____ elephant   _____ chair

_____ apple   _____ movie

_____ day   _____ monster

Use adjectives to finish the sentences.

We had a _____ lunch at the _____ park.

I got into my _____ bed and read my _____book.

I am wearing a _____ shirt and a _____ jumper.

What do these children want to be when they are older?

chef, garda, gardener, hairdresser, astronaut, fireman, artist, vet

I want to put out fires and save people.

I want to catch bad people and send them to jail.

I want to make sick animals better.

I want to cut people's hair.

I want to cook delicious meals.

I want to make beautiful gardens.

I want to fly into space.

I want to paint pictures.

What do you want to be when you grow up? _____

_____

What kind of things do you think you will be doing?

_____

_____

When you are older, what things will you do? What things won't you do? Write a list. Draw a picture to match your list.

When I'm older........

I_____

_____

_____

_____

_____

_____

_____

_____

_____

_____

11

Big Ted's Barbecue

Read this part of the story.

'I'll have a barbecue,' said Big Ted. 'Tom, Bill, Vera and Tony can come to my house.'

Big Ted said 'I want some meat for my barbecue.' So Big Ted went shopping. 'I want all kinds of meat for my barbecue,' Big Ted said to Alex the butcher. Big Ted and Alex chose the meat for the barbecue.

Later, Big Ted took out the meat. He took out the barbecue. He put out some paper plates. He put out all his knives and forks. He put on a hat and an apron. 'Now I'm ready to cook,' said Big Ted. Tom, Bill, Vera and Tony came to Big Ted's house. 'Good to see you,' said Big Ted.

'What would you like?' Big Ted said to Tom the bus driver.

'Sausages, please,' said Tom.

So Big Ted put some sausages on the barbecue.

Draw all the things Ted put onto the barbecue.

Answer the questions. Use full sentences.

What did Ted buy when he went shopping?

_____

What did Ted put out for the barbecue?

_____

What did Tom want on the barbecue?

_____

What job did Bill have?

_____

Who wanted chicken on the barbecue?

_____

What happened to the barbecue?

_____

Do you think the fire was Ted's fault? Say why/why not.

_____

What do you think happened after Ted put out the fire?

_____

What do you like to have on the barbecue?

_____

Write the order of things that Ted put on the barbecue.

1. _____   2. _____

3. _____   4. _____

Complete the wordsearch.

off, would, want, some, barbecue, meat, ready, sausages, cook, doctor, vet, driver, hairdresser, please, too

f	d	r	p	f	a	w	o	u	l	d	v
t	h	h	b	a	r	b	e	c	u	e	m
s	a	u	s	a	g	e	s	r	m	y	f
v	i	z	m	b	s	o	m	e	w	m	o
j	r	b	o	p	t	x	e	a	z	z	f
n	d	o	c	t	o	r	a	d	t	v	f
c	r	v	e	t	o	z	t	y	j	j	v
c	e	y	f	s	z	g	i	w	a	k	z
o	s	n	k	m	p	l	e	a	s	e	u
o	s	k	u	u	w	v	g	n	a	g	z
k	e	k	i	u	p	y	q	t	l	t	k
k	r	c	d	r	i	v	e	r	x	s	v

Choose meet or meat.

Example: I am going to **meet** my friend in town. We are going to the supermarket to buy **meat** and vegetables.

I am going to _____ my friend at the shop.

The parents are going to _____ the teachers today.

You can buy _____ from the butchers.

I am very pleased to _____ you.

My sister does not eat any _____.

63

Write the jobs these people do.

doctor, nurse, chef, teacher, hairdresser,
bus driver, builder, vet, fireman

_____

_____

_____

_____

_____

_____

_____

_____

_____

What job would you like to do one day?

_____

Finish the recipe on how to barbecue chicken.

pepper, enjoy, until, chicken, hot, coals, ten, sauce, barbecue

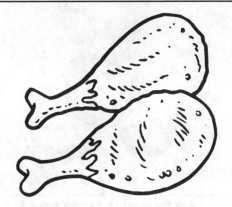

How to barbecue chicken

1. First buy some pieces of _____.

2. Place the chicken pieces in a barbecue _____.

3. Ask an adult to start burning the _____ in the barbecue.

4. Wait until the coals are _____.

5. Put salt and _____ on the chicken.

6. Put the chicken on the _____.

7. Grill the chicken on both sides _____ cooked.

8. Leave the chicken for _____ minutes.

9. Eat and _____!

Do you like barbecue chicken? Say why or why not.

_____

_____

_____

_____

Imagine you were applying for a job. Fill in the form.

Use capital letters.

JOB APPLICATION
Please use BLOCK CAPITALS.

Surname	
First name	
Address	
Telephone number	
Date of birth	
Which job are you applying for?	
Why do you want this job?	
Name some things you are good at.	
Signature:	

  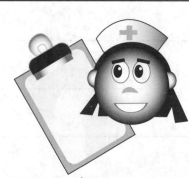

12

Advertisement

Complete the poster. Use your own words.

New arcade opening!

Tell your .... and come join in!

This weekend, all games are **HALF PRICE!**

Loads of prizes, loads of ...., loads of fun!

Arcade games, 3D XD theatre, bowling alley, mini-golf,

pool tables, and

....

....

....

Which activities will you choose?

Light meals, snacks and .... available.

Don't delay, come today!

Entry fee: .... euro

The Wild Side, 10 Main Street

Visit us on the website:

www.fireworksenglish.ie/wildside or write to us.

Answer the questions. Use full sentences.

What special offer do they have this weekend?

_____

Name two things you can do there.

_____

_____

Can you buy something to eat at this arcade?

_____

How much does it cost to get in?

_____

What is the arcade called?

_____

Where is the arcade?

_____

Write down the website address.

_____

What other things do you think you could do there?

_____

Would you like to go to this arcade? Say why/why not.

_____

_____

Finish the sentences.

> don't, your, which, write, us, tell, five

You must _____ your Mum where you are going.

Do you ever fight with _____ sister?

I do not know _____ puzzle to choose.

Please _____ put your feet on the table.

There were _____ baby birds in the nest.

My cousin sent _____ a postcard from Paris.

The teacher says we must _____ neatly.

Write the full words.

> I am, will not, I will, cannot, have not, do not

can't _____   don't _____

won't _____   I'm _____

I'll _____   haven't _____

Write two sentences using shortened words.

_____

_____

Remember we use capital letters at the beginning of a sentence, for the word I, for names of people and places and for days of the week and months of the year. We use a full stop at the end of a sentence.

Circle the letters that should be capital letters. Add full stops to the end of the sentences.

my friend luke is going to spain in the summer

on tuesday the class is going on a trip to dublin

paul and amy are dressing up for st. patrick's day

i think i will have a party for my birthday in august

shauna and her family are diving to cork on Saturday

Write the words in the correct column.

table, talk, sleep, Liam, cry, teddy, games, Main Street, play, eat

Nouns	Verbs

Write your own verb. _____

Write your own noun. _____

Look at this advert for a waterpark.

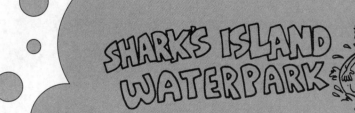

Come and enjoy our NEW park!

Including:
Pirates Cove, Toddler's Section,
Super Bowl, Boomerang,
Decking area and much, much more!

€15 for the whole day!

Shark's Island Waterpark, Ocean Road, Dublin
Tel: 01 32454524

Where is this park? _____

How much does it cost for a day ticket? _____

Is this an old or a new park? _____

What is the telephone number? _____

Is there a ride called the Boomerang? _____

Do you think this is a good advert? Say why or why not.

_____

_____

Would you like to go here?

_____

_____

Write your own advertisement for an exciting waterpark.

waterpark

rides

scary

swimming pool

wave pool

waterslides

high

entry fee

opening times

telephone

restaurant

splash

games

fun

address

website

rubber tubes

13

The Hundred-Mile-an-Hour Dog

Write the names of these characters in the story.

Tina, Mouse, Streaker, Trevor

_____

_____

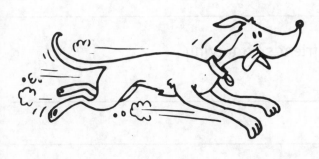

_____

_____

Write one sentence about each.

Trevor _____

_____

_____

_____

Answer the questions. Use full sentences.

Why did some children make fun of Trevor?

_____

When did Tina and Trevor become friends?

_____

Who do you think won the wrestling competition that Tina and Trevor had? Say why you think so.

_____

_____

Who is Mouse?

_____

Name three things that Streaker had put in the bed.

_____

Do you think that Trevor and Tina are good friends? Say why.

_____

_____

Do you think Tina will be able to teach Streaker? Say why.

_____

_____

What do you think might happen next?

_____

How do you think the story will end?

_____

Prepositions make links between words. Example: The mouse is hiding <u>under</u> my bed.

Other examples of prepositions: in, on, out, with, by, up, between, near, on, off, after, below, with

Underline the prepositions in these sentences.

The dog swam in the river.

My pet sleeps on my bed.

The birds flew around the cage.

The horse jumped over the gate.

Choose the correct preposition.

from, about, through, before, to, onto, near, behind

The dog jumped _____ the sofa.

I have to do my homework _____ I can watch TV.

Mum got a letter _____ the school.

We live _____ the town centre.

My friend sits _____ me in class.

I am reading a book _____ aliens.

The plane flew _____ the clouds.

I wrote a letter _____ to my cousin in America.

This piece of writing is full of mistakes. There are missing capital letters, full stops and question marks. There are also some incorrect capital letters. Can you mark it? Correct the mistakes.

there once was a boy called trevor

he had a friend called tina.

their birthday was on the same day in june

Tina is taller than Trevor

tina has lots of freckles

Tina has a dog called mouse and trevor has a dog called streaker

Mouse is a very big Dog.

Streaker sleeps in Trevor's Bed.

do you have a pet at home

Write some good pet names for these pets.

dog   _____

snake   _____

fish   _____

bird   _____

rabbit   _____

lion   _____

Finish the sentences.

> friend, shared, taller, competition,
> because, head, intelligent, might, pairs

Some dogs are very _____ and you can teach them tricks.

A giraffe is _____ than I am.

The cake was _____ among the children.

My cat likes to be patted on the _____.

We are going for a walk _____ it is a nice day.

Our class is taking part in a singing _____.

The teacher _____ take us to the museum soon.

I have two _____ of white runners.

My best _____ is called Kevin.

How many words can you make with these letters?

i	l	o
v	e	m
a	r	m
i	t	e

_____

_____

_____

_____

_____

Write an 'I am an animal' poem.

Method _____

Line 1 I am | write the name of an animal here |

Line 2 | color | as | compare the color to something else |

Line 3 I | verb | | describe something your animal does |

Line 4 I | verb | | describe something else your animal does |

Line 5 I can | describe something your animal does well |

Line 6 I can | describe something else your animal is able to do well |

Line 7 I am (repeat from line 1)

Example: **Your turn**

I am a camel   _____

Light brown as the desert sand   _____

I carry you   _____

I carry your bags   _____

I can go ages without water   _____

I can spit at you when I am mad!   _____

I am a camel   _____

14

The Goat that Hated Vegetables

Read this part of the story.

Once upon a time, there was a goat called Stan. He hated vegetables. His family said to him, 'All goats eat vegetables! Vegetables are a goat's favourite thing.'

'I don't like vegetables!' said the goat.

The family came up with a plan.

On Monday, they hid some carrots in his sandwich. 'This sandwich does not taste nice!' said Stan, and he gave the sandwich to his sister.

On Tuesday, they hid some cabbage in the stew. 'This stew is not yummy!' said Stan, and he gave the stew to his brother.

On Wednesday, the family hid some spinach in his burger. 'This burger tastes funny!' said Stan. He gave it to his Mum.

Write what the goats are saying.

Answer the questions. Use full sentences.

What is the name of the main character in the story?

_____

What does the family want him to do?

_____

What was their plan?

_____

Why did Stan not want vegetable soup?

_____

What did the family do on the Wednesday?

_____

Why do you think Stan tasted the vegetables on Sunday?

_____

Did Stan like the vegetables? How do you know?

_____

Can you name another story that has goats in it?

_____

What is your favourite vegetable?

_____

Write a diary for the goat family on what they did each day. Write what Stan did on the Sunday. Remember to use a capital letter at the beginning of a sentence and a full stop at the end of the sentence.

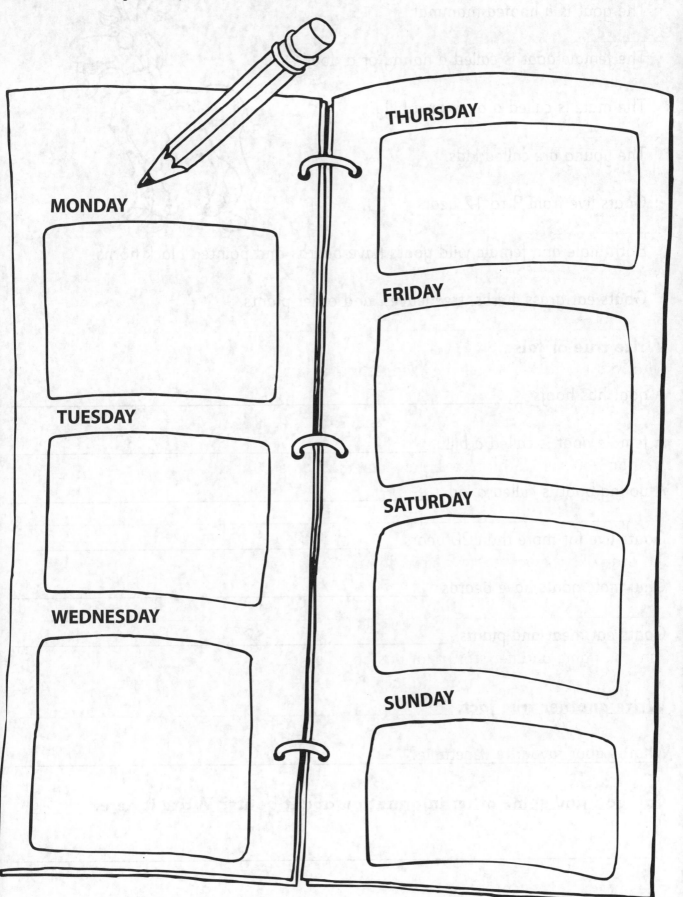

MONDAY

TUESDAY

WEDNESDAY

THURSDAY

FRIDAY

SATURDAY

SUNDAY

Read the facts about goats.

- The goat is a hoofed mammal.

- The female goat is called a nanny or a doe.

- The male is called a buck or a billy.

- The young are called kids.

- Goats live from 9 to 12 years.

- Both male and female wild goats have beards and pointed black horns.

- Goats eat grass, herbs, tree leaves, and other plants.

Write true or false.

A goat has hoofs. _____

A female goat is called a billy. _____

A young goat is called a kid. _____

Goats live for more than 20 years._____

Only male goats have beards. _____

Goats eat meat and plants. _____

Write another true fact.

_____

Can you find some other information about goats? Write it here.

_____

_____

Complete the crossword.

Across

1. p _ _ _ p k _ n

4. c _ _ c _ _ m _ e _

5. t _ m _ t _

7. c _ r _

8. p _ t _ t _

Down

2. m _ _ s h _ _ _ _ m

3. c _ _ b _ _ _ g _

4. c _ _ r r _ t

6. o _ _ _ _ n

If you were making a crossword, write one clue and answer you could use.

_____

_____

Write your own instruction manual.

Write instructions on how to plant tomatoes. Look at the pictures to help you.

Things you need

potting soil   pot   tomato seeds

Method

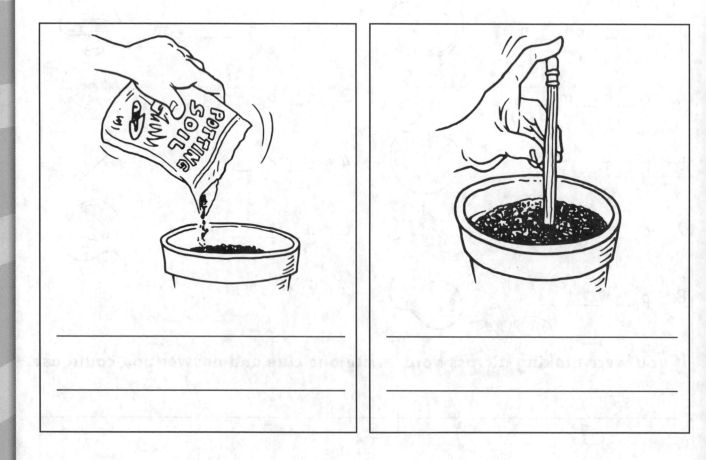

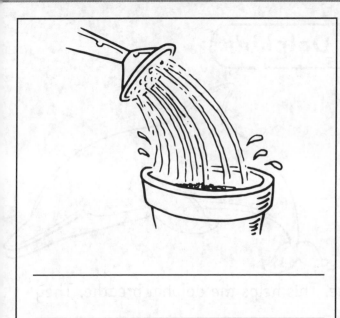

_____

_____

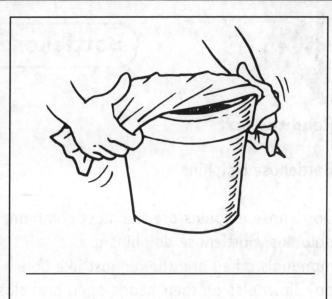

_____

_____

_____

_____

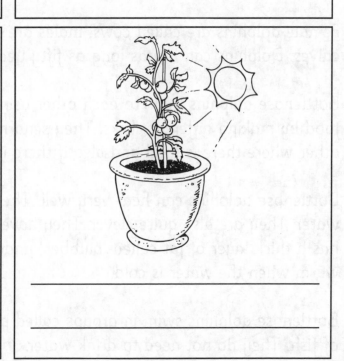

_____

_____

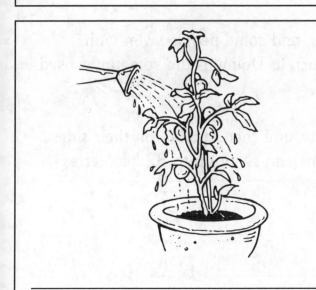

_____

_____

15

Bottlenose Dolphins

Read the text.

Bottlenose Dolphins

Bottlenose dolphins are the most common dolphins. Bottlenose dolphins are mammals. They breathe air, just like you do. Blowholes on their heads open and close. This helps the dolphin breathe. They can stay under water for up to 15 minutes.

Female dolphins are called cows, males are called bulls and baby dolphins are called calves. Dolphins can live as long as fifty years.

Bottlenose dolphins 'talk' to each other using different noises. They can even find food by making different clicks. They send messages to each other. They tell each other where there is food and also if there is danger.

Bottlenose dolphins can hear very well. They can also see very well, in and out of water. They are also quite clever. They have bigger brains than we do! A dolphin has a thick layer of fat called 'blubber' under the skin. This fat keeps the dolphin warm when the water is cold.

Bottlenose dolphins swim in groups called pods. Dolphins will eat almost any kind of fish. They do not need to drink water.

Sometimes dolphins can be friendly to humans, and some people swim with dolphins. Their skin feels smooth when you touch it. Dolphins are sometimes used in shows and they can do tricks.

Dolphins have been seen jumping high in the air and then landing on their sides or back with a great splash. Bottlenose dolphins can swim up to 32 kilometres per hour.

Underline all the plural words.

Answer the questions. Use full sentences.

Which dolphins are the most common?

_____

How does the blowhole help the dolphin?

_____

What are male dolphins called?

_____

What helps to keep a dolphin warm?

_____

Do dolphins drink water?

_____

Name one way in which dolphins can be friendly to humans.

_____

_____

Why do you think that people like dolphins so much?

_____

_____

Would you like to be a dolphin? Say why/why not.

_____

_____

Read the sentences. Use a tick (✔) or a cross (✘) under Humans and Dolphins to see how humans and dolphins are similar.

	Humans	Dolphins
They live in pods.		
They live in the sea or rivers.		
They breathe air.		
They send messages to each other.		
They do not drink water.		
They eat fish.		
They are mammals.		
They can stay under water for 15 minutes.		
They are clever.		
They have teeth.		
They can do tricks.		
They talk with words.		

How many were the same for humans and dolphins?

_____

Write the definition for these. Use a dictionary if you need to.

bottlenose dolphin _____

blubber _____

mammal _____

blowhole _____

orca _____

nap _____

communicate _____

Groups of things sometimes have special words.

Example: a deck of cards, a pack of wolves, a school of fish

Write the correct group name for these:

> pride, flight, pack, army, rainbow, swarm,
> clutch, troop, gaggle, pod, flock, herd

An _____ of ants

A _____ of monkeys

A _____ of bees

A _____ of sheep

A _____ of dogs

A _____ of stairs

A _____ of elephants

A _____ of geese

A _____ of lions

A _____ of eggs

A _____ of dolphins

A _____ of butterflies

Make up two of your own.

_____

_____

Imagine that you were a dolphin. Write about one day in your life.

Think about:

- What you do in the day

- What you eat

- Who you meet

- Good or bad things that might happen

_____

_____

_____

_____

_____

_____

_____

_____

_____

_____

_____